Across the Curric
GEOGRAPHY
for ages 8 – 9

Introduction

Across the Curriculum Geography provides a wide range of specially devised photocopiable worksheets, based on the QCA geography units, that can be used to address other curriculum areas when teaching geography. Alternatively, you may prefer to use the worksheets when teaching other subjects, in the knowledge that you are also covering valuable aspects of the geography curriculum.

For most of the units in this book there is a topic web and a set of Teacher's Notes. The topic web refers to possible links that can be made to other subjects, to help you with your planning, but you may well come up with more ideas and these can be added to the web as you go along. The Teacher's Notes provide background information on the worksheets and details of the Numeracy and Literacy and other curriculum objectives that each sheet is likely to cover. A summary of these objectives is provided on the Contents page overleaf.

Some sheets, which do not have a specific geographical content, are included because the geography topic provides obvious and important links to aspects of other subjects.

Many of the worksheets will be invaluable for speaking and listening – an important aspect of English in the National Curriculum that is not always addressed through the Literacy Strategy. Most of the worksheets can be used as a focus for small group activities and are ideal for children working with teaching assistants.

Contents and Curriculum Links

WORKSHEET	GEOGRAPHY	OTHER CURRICULUM OBJECTIVES
Improving the environment 1	2a	Literacy: Term 1 Word 12, Term 2 Word 12
Improving the environment 2	5a, 5b	DT: 1a, 2a, 2c, 3d, 3e, 4a, 4b, 4c, 5c
Improving the environment 3	5a, 5b	DT: 1a, 2a, 2c, 3d, 3e, 4a, 4b, 4c, 5c
Village settlers 1	3d, 3e, 3f	Literacy: Term 2 Word 11; History 4, 9
Village settlers 2	2c, 3d	Literacy: Term 2 Word 11; History 4, 9
Village settlers 3	2c, 3d	Literacy: Term 2 Word 11; History 4, 9
Village settlers 4	3a, 3c, 3d	Numeracy: Calculations
A village in India 1	2d, 3a, 3d, 3f	English Speaking and Listening – Key skills 1b, 2a
A village in India 2	2c, 2e	Literacy: Term 1, 2 and 3 Word 1
A village in India 3	2c, 2e	Literacy: Term 1, 2 and 3 Word 1
Using our spare time 1	2a	Literacy: Term 1, 2 and 3 Word 1
Using our spare time 2	1c	Numeracy: Handling Data
Using our spare time 3	3a, 3d	Science 4: Physical Processes 2c
Improving our area 1	2c, 2d	Art: 1a
Improving our area 2	2c, 2d	Art: 1a
Improving our area 3	2e, 3a, 3d, 5a, 5b	Literacy: Term 1, 2 and 3 Word 1
Improving our area 4	1a, 1b, 1c, 1d, 1e, 2a, 2d, 2g, 3a, 3d, 3e, 4b, 5a	History 4a, 4b, 5c, 7; Literacy Term 1 Text 27, Term 3 Text 21, 23; English Speaking and Listening
What's in the news? 1	1c, 2a, 2c, 3b, 7a	English Speaking and Listening 1, 2, 6a, 8, 9
What's in the news? 2	1c, 2a, 2c, 3b, 7a	English Speaking and Listening 1, 2, 6a, 8, 9
Connections across the world 1	1b, 1c, 2a, 2b, 2d	Numeracy: Fractions
Connections across the world 2	1c, 2a, 2d	Numeracy: Handling data
Connections across the world 3	1c, 2a, 2d	Numeracy: Handling data
Connections across the world 4	2a, 3a	Literacy Term 1 Text 19 and 27
Our whole world 1	2c, 3b	Literacy: Terms 1, 2 and 3 Word 3; History 9, 13
Our whole world 2	1b, 1c, 2d, 3a	Literacy: Term 1 Text 22, Term 2 Text 17
Our whole world 3	1b, 1c, 2d, 3a	Literacy: Term 1 Text 22, Term 2 Text 17
Our whole world 4	1b, 1c, 2d, 3a	Literacy: Term 1 Text 22, Term 2 Text 17
Our whole world 5	1b, 1c, 2d, 3a	Literacy: Term 1 Text 22, Term 2 Text 17
Geography and numbers 1	2a	Numeracy: Shape and Space; Literacy: vocabulary – mnemonic
Geography and numbers 2	2a	Numeracy: Shape and Space
Geography and numbers 3	2a	Numeracy: Shape and Space; Calculations; Data Handling; Numbers and the Number System – fractions of numbers

Improving the environment

CURRICULUM LINKS

This topic web shows possible curriculum links but we will not have thought of everything so you may like to add some of your own.

LITERACY
- Topic based vocabulary development (Worksheet 1)
- Writing newspaper style reports

NUMERACY
- Weighing rubbish produced in school (no food waste or other potentially hazardous materials)
- Graphs of types/amounts of rubbish per day

ART
- Produce a piece of art to represent a journey. Use 'clean rubbish' to create this art work

SCIENCE
- Use of materials for insulation
- Use of 'clean litter' for experiments – eg paper, cans, bottles, packaging

ICT
- Create a magazine article on the importance of recycling

Improving the environment

DT
- Design and make bins for school use, considering opening mechanisms (Worksheet 2, 3)

RE
- Investigate the attitudes of local religious groups to environmental issues

HISTORY
- Investigate the types of rubbish produced in the past – eg in World War 2 or 100 years ago – how and why the rubbish we produce has changed

Improving the environment

(QCA Unit 8: Improving the environment)

Worksheet 1 (**LITERACY**) introduces some of the geographical vocabulary needed for this topic. Children are asked to arrange the words provided in alphabetical order – this will involve sorting by third and fourth letters. They are also asked to create simple definitions for each word. We recommend that this should be the focus of a class discussion where children are asked to make suggestions for definitions. The following ideas may be of help to them:

bin	a container for rubbish or litter
community	a group of people working together
compost	old rotted vegetation that helps plants grow
conservation	ensuring that the environment does not suffer through changes
litter	carelessly discarded rubbish
pollution	harmful substances affecting the environment
recycling	using materials again
waste	rubbish, litter

Worksheets 2 and 3 (**DT**) are concerned with the appropriate use of litter bins. Worksheet 2 is suitable for group use or for use with an OHP. The design and making of a bin with some type of lid or flap will address the 'mechanisms' element of Year 4 DT. Whilst DT forms the focus of this work, there are also mathematical aspects, such as accurate measurements and drawing to scale.

The work can be enhanced by showing pupils a range of types of bin used in a variety of settings. It is expected that pupils would be given the opportunity to make scale models using materials available in the classroom, even though in most cases it would be impractical to produce the real thing.

Improving the environment 1

Name: Date:

In the word bank below are some words that you may need to know in your work on improving the environment. Arrange the words in alphabetical order and write a simple definition beside each word.

WORD BANK

community

conservation

pollution recycling

litter   waste bin

compost

Each definition should be written in only a few words.

word	definition
_____	_____
_____	_____
_____	_____
_____	_____
_____	_____
_____	_____

Improving the environment 2

Name: Date:

Putting litter in bins is one way we can help to improve our environment.

When designing bins there are several factors to consider.

Add your own notes to the boxes below.

The size your bin will need to be:
- think about the amount of litter that may be put in the bin each day
- think about the height of the children using each bin

What your bin should be made from:
- it will need to be weatherproof if it is for outdoor use
- it should be easy to clean

What your bin will look like:
- your bin should be attractive
- your bin should be clearly seen to encourage use

Whether your bin will need a lid:
- think about how the lid will open easily
- think about how the lid can be used hygenically

Improving the environment 3

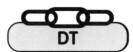

Name: _____   Date: _____

Design a bin for use in school.

Label your design with measurements, materials and mechanisms.

My design is for use in _____

Village settlers

This topic web shows possible curriculum links but we will not have thought of everything so you may like to add some of your own.

LITERACY
- Introduction to prefixes and suffixes
- Changes in language over time
(Worksheet 2)

NUMERACY
- Adding pairs of two digit numbers
(Worksheet 4)

ICT
- Writing factual information about towns with particular types of names linked to their history

SCIENCE
- Keeping warm – ways people kept warm in the past (based on invaders being studied)
- Habitats – chosen habitats for humans in the past

ART
- Investigating art work of invaders and settlers in the local area

Village settlers

HISTORY
- Invaders and settlers – Anglo-Saxons, Vikings, Romans
(Worksheet 1, 3)

Village settlers

(QCA Unit 9: Village settlers)

Worksheet 1 (**HISTORY**) is suitable for individual, group or whole class use (with use of an OHP). Pupils are encouraged to discuss place names and how spellings may have changed over the centuries. It is important to discuss how we find early references to town or village names – for example, through church records, the Domesday Book, etc. This information sheet also provides the starting point for discussing why settlers may have chosen particular places to settle.

Worksheets 2 and 3 (HISTORY)
Ask the children to use the information from worksheet 1 to categorize a selection of town names and to mark the positions of six of them on a map. Using the facts from worksheet 1, the pupils should be able to sort the towns as follows:

Anglo-Saxon: Birmingham, Aylesbury, Southampton, Bury
Roman: Chesterfield, Lancaster, Gloucester, Stratford-upon-Avon
Viking: Scunthorpe, Redcar, Derby, Grimsby

You may wish children also to complete an extension activity of finding four more place names to add to each category and to place on the map. Colour coding the categories may help class discussion on the way invaders entered Britain and travelled through areas.

Worksheet 4 (**NUMERACY**) gives children more facts about place names and reinforces pupils' ability to calculate mentally with pairs of two digit numbers. You may wish to use this sheet as a preliminary activity to asking pupils to investigate place names in your locality. The answers are as follows:

1. ford (94, 35, 67, 62)
2. worth (37, 35, 67, 42, 56)
3. cot (99, 35, 42)
4. ley (72, 88, 50)
5. stoke (39, 42, 35, 77, 88)
6. feld (94, 88, 72, 62)

Village settlers 1

Name: Date:

Place names from history

Most towns and villages in Great Britain have names that have changed very little for hundreds of years. All of the names given to them have meanings, some of which were brought to us by the people who invaded the country in the past.

The invaders needed to settle in places where there was water to drink, areas of good soil to plant crops and rivers to travel along. Many place names give us clues to why each settlement began.

Have you ever wondered how a town or village near you first got its name?

Here are some facts to help you to find out.

- The Anglo-Saxon word **ham** meant homestead.
- The word **bury** or **burgh** meant manor house or stronghold.
- **Tun**, often spelt **ton**, meant farm.

The Vikings also helped name some towns and villages.

- **By** meant a farm or village.
- **Thorp** meant a remote farm or hamlet.
- **Car** was an area of marshy land.

The Romans also helped us name some towns.

- Anywhere with **caster**, **cester** or **chester** was probably a Roman fort or walled town.
- **Strat, street** or **streat** in a place name indicates that it was close to a Roman road.

You will need these facts for Worksheet 2.

       Andrew Brodie: Across the Curriculum Geography 8–9 © A & C Black Publishers Ltd

Village settlers 2

Name: Date:

 Sort the place names from the word bank into the correct sets below.

WORD BANK

Chesterfield Derby Grimsby Birmingham Aylesbury

Redcar Bury Southampton Scunthorpe

Stratford-upon-Avon Gloucester Lancaster

Anglo-Saxon names

Viking names

Roman names

Village settlers 3

Name: Date:

Write the names of these places in the correct positions on the map: Grimsby, Birmingham, Southampton, Scunthorpe, Gloucester, Lancaster. You will need an atlas to help you.

Colour the circles by each place name using this colour code:

Red – Anglo-Saxon   Blue – Roman   Green - Viking

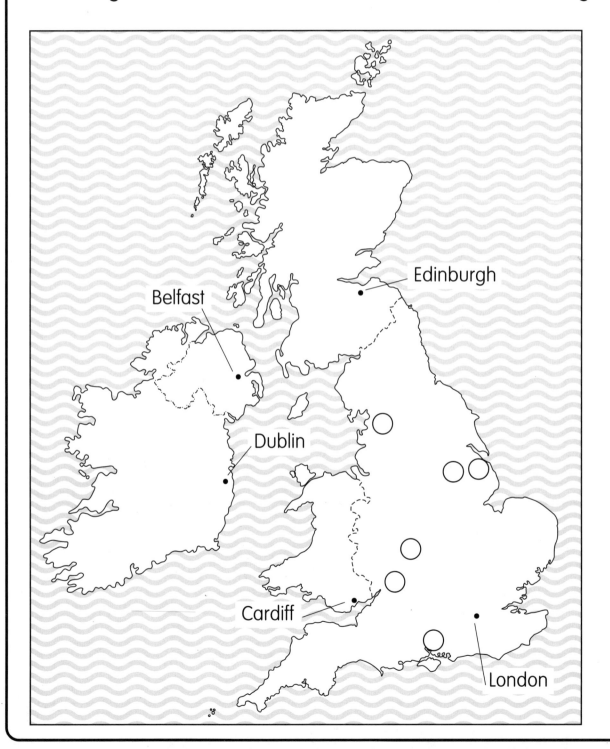

Andrew Brodie: Across the Curriculum Geography 8–9 © A & C Black Publishers Ltd

Village settlers   4

Name: _____   Date: _____

Find the missing words or word parts. You will need to do some mental maths, then find the letter that matches each answer. The letters that you find will make words that are all connected with place names.

33	17	99	62	88	94	21	56	66	45	77	72	48
A	B	C	D	E	F	G	H	I	J	K	L	M

26	35	11	22	67	39	42	16	97	37	69	50	90
N	O	P	Q	R	S	T	U	V	W	X	Y	Z

1. _ _ _ _
   43 + 51
   17 + 18
   21 + 46
   33 + 29

2. _ _ _ _ _
   24 + 13
   10 + 25
   58 + 9
   21+ 21
   26 + 30

3. _ _ _
   66 + 33
   14 + 21
   24 + 18

4. _ _ _
   49 + 23
   43 + 45
   29 + 21

5. _ _ _ _ _
   24 + 15
   17 + 25
   11 + 24
   44 + 33
   21 + 67

6. _ _ _ _
   72 + 22
   29 + 59
   58 + 14
   23 + 39

1. _ _ _ _ means a river crossing.

2. _ _ _ _ _ means an enclosed settlement.

3. _ _ _ means cottage.

4. _ _ _ means a glade or clearing in the woods.

5. _ _ _ _ _ means a hamlet or outlying farm.

6. _ _ _ _ means an open area of land (or field).

Andrew Brodie: Across the Curriculum Geography 8–9 © A & C Black Publishers Ltd

A village in India

(QCA Unit 10: A village in India)

Please note that as this is a short unit we have not included a topic web. However you may wish to consider other curriculum links:

RE – link to Year 4 work on how and why Hindus worship at home.

Art – study Indian art.

Science
- habitats/keeping warm: linking types of housing with Indian climate.
- crops grown for balanced diets.

The purpose of the work in this unit is to enhance pupils' understanding of work they may have already done on Indian village life by putting it in the wider context of India and its place in the world.

Pupils are encouraged to reflect on the great differences in town and country life in India, and the effect of modern western technology on ways of life.

Worksheet 1 (LITERACY) asks children to discuss a given picture and to use reasoning and knowledge when considering it. The children should work in pairs for this activity. (The photograph was taken in Puna in November 2004.) As an extension, children may be asked to present written reports on what they have discussed – they could use the computer to do this.

Worksheets 2 and 3 (LITERACY) ask pupils to mark features on a map. These features include the Himalayas, though pupils should understand that only the foothills are in India and that the main part of the range is in Nepal; Everest is on the border of China and Nepal.

A village in India 1

Name: Date:

Work with a partner.

Look at the picture below and discuss it with your partner.

Here are some things to think about:

> The picture was taken in India in November 2004.
>
> Do you think the picture was taken in a town or a village?
>
> What features of the photograph tell you that it was not taken in Great Britain?

Prepare a short talk to report your conclusions to the rest of your class.

A village in India   2

Name: Date:

Use the map on Worksheet 3. This page gives you instructions regarding the map. You will also need an atlas to help you.

1. Shade the British Isles red.

2. Shade all the sea blue.

3. Find India on the map, then label the following features:

    (a) New Dheli (the capital city of India)

    (b) The Himalayas (This mountain range is only partly in India. Use an atlas to find out which other countries share this mountain range.)

    (c) Sri Lanka (an island near the southern tip of India)

4. Now draw lines on the map to show:

    (a) The Equator

    (b) The Tropic of Cancer (in the Northern hemisphere)

    (c) The Tropic of Capricorn (in the Southern hemisphere)

5. Shade India yellow.

6. Shade all other land areas green.

7. Complete the colour key beside the map.

   Andrew Brodie: Across the Curriculum Geography 8–9 © A & C Black Publishers Ltd

A village in India   3

Name: Date:

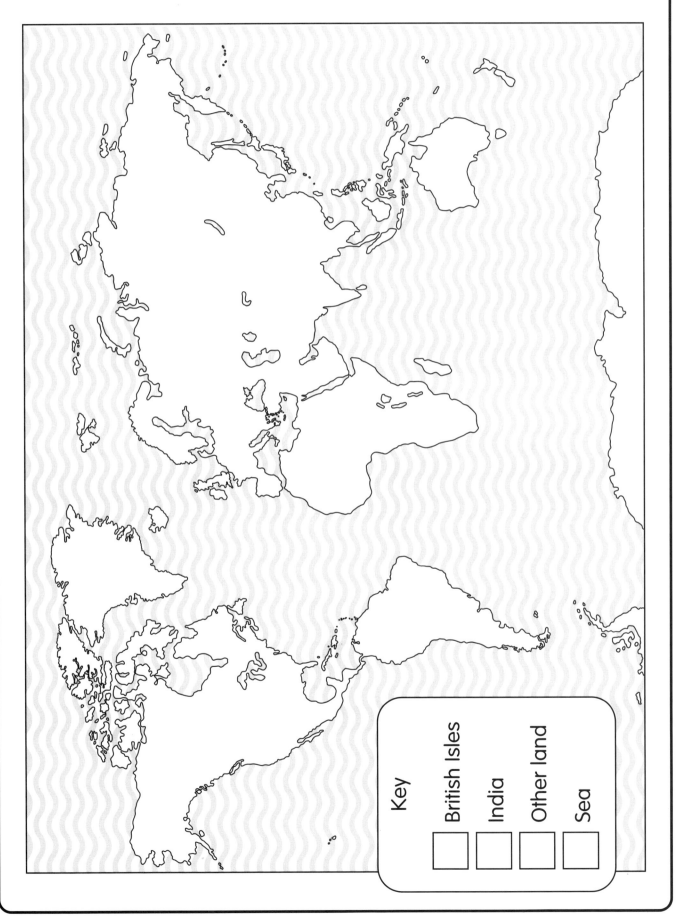

Key

British Isles ☐

India ☐

Other land ☐

Sea ☐

Using our spare time

This topic web shows possible curriculum links but we will not have thought of everything so you may like to add some of your own.

LITERACY
- Topic vocabulary (Worksheet 1)
- Speaking and Listening: two minute talk on 'my leisure activities'

NUMERACY
- Averaging time spent on particular leisure activities (Worksheet 2)

PE
- Appropriate conditions/clothing to best enjoy a variety of sporting activities

SCIENCE
- Leisure activities and personal health
- Friction in sporting and leisure activities (Worksheet 3)

ART
- Design and make a sculpture representing a leisure activity

Using our spare time

HISTORY
- Investigation of leisure pursuits connected with time/people being studied

ICT
- Design logo to represent a chosen leisure activity; use graphics package to form repeating pattern picture from the logo designed

MUSIC
- Use of classroom instruments/ voices to create music describing sports/leisure activities
- Pupils who play conventional instruments to have the opportunity to use them in school and to explain to peers why they have chosen to learn to play

Using our spare time

(QCA Unit 19: How and where do we spend our time?)

Worksheet 1 (**LITERACY**) is a language based sheet providing an introduction to the variety of leisure activities that can be enjoyed. The 'alphabetical challenge' can be completed on the reverse of the sheet and provides another opportunity for pupils to use a dictionary, finding names of activities and spelling them correctly. It is important that pupils realise that they may not be able to find an activity for every letter of the alphabet. Further tasks could include categorizing activities; pupils inventing leisure activity puzzles for their peers to complete; listing activities that are catered for in the locality of the school. The answers to the puzzle are as follows: 1. tennis; 2. rugby; 3. art; 4. horse riding; 5. skiing; 6. walking; 7. netball; 8. knitting; 9. singing.

Worksheet 2 (**NUMERACY**) provides an introduction to finding the 'mean' average as recommended in the QCA Unit for Year 4, 'How and where do we spend our time'. The mean is normally introduced at Year 6 but is within the ability of younger mathematically able pupils, where it is presented in a realistic situation. We suggest that this activity is completed by a small group of higher attaining pupils with the support of an adult, discussing the terms 'average' and 'mean'. Ideally the group should calculate their own mean average for a particular activity that all members of the group enjoy, though it is unlikely that all members will participate in a specific sport or leisure activity apart from watching television!

Each child in the group could be asked to state how many hours that they participate in a particular activity over the course of a week or during one evening, to the nearest half hour.

The results should be totalled, then divided by the number of pupils in the group to produce the mean. The children will need to be told very clearly that the result that they have found is what most people call the 'average'. 'On average, people in this group watch ... hours of television each evening.' They should be encouraged to observe that some people spend more than the average time and some spend less.

Worksheet 3 (**SCIENCE**) links geography in relation to leisure activities with science work on friction and forces and encourages pupils to consider what they have learnt. This sheet is suitable for use as an assessment activity for pupils' scientific work on friction, pushes and pulls, air resistance and gravity.

Using our spare time   1

LITERACY

Name:

Date:

An activity that we choose to do in our spare time is known as a leisure activity.

Leisure activities may be forms of sport, music making, hobbies or anything else we enjoy doing.

Follow the clues to complete the puzzle. You may need to use a dictionary to help you to spell the words. At least one letter has been put into each word to help you.

Clues across

4. Sit in the saddle and hold the reins while doing this (5, 6)
7. A team game, score by throwing a ball into a net at the top of a post (7)
8. Wool and needles are used to make scarves, jumpers, etc. (8)
9. Do this alone or in a choir (7)

Clues down

1. This is played with racquets, a ball and a net (6)
2. A game similar to football but played with an oval ball (5)
3. Painting, drawing and sculpture are all forms of this (3)
4. Use 'sticks' to hit the ball towards the goal in this game (6)
5. Sliding down snowy slopes (6)
6. Some people go miles doing this; some even take their dogs! (7)

Alphabetical challenge.

Try to think of a leisure activity for each letter of the alphabet. For example: T - tennis

Name: Date:

Six children enjoy playing football.

They worked out the **mean** time they spend playing football each week. The mean is a type of average.

Firstly they added their times together:

1.5 + 2.5 + 1 + 1.5 + 1 + 1.5 = 9

Then, because there were six children the total was divided by 6:

9 ÷ 6 = 1.5

So the mean was 1.5

Alan	1.5 hours
Bill	2.5 hours
Caz	1 hour
Dot	1.5 hours
Ellie	1 hour
Finn	1.5 hours

Now see if you can work out the means for the following leisure activities. You may use a calculator if you need to.

Hours watching TV last night	
Abi	3 hours
Bob	2 hours
Connor	4 hours
Debbie	3 hours

There are four children so this time you need to divide the total by 4.

Mean =

Time spent drawing and painting each week	
Amy	3 hours
Brian	2 hours
Cally	1 hour
Dean	2.5 hours
Ed	3 hours
Fay	1 hour
Gus	1.5 hours
Hal	1 hour
Ivy	3 hours
Jasdeep	2 hours

Mean =

Now find out the mean time that you and three of your friends spend watching television.

Using our spare time 3

Name: _____   Date: _____

Look at the pictures below. Each picture shows someone enjoying a leisure activity. In each picture look for the parts played by forces and friction. Write about the forces and friction for each picture.

_____

_____

_____

_____

_____

_____

_____

_____

_____

_____

_____

_____

Write a few sentences to answer these questions:

Are there any of these activities that cannot be enjoyed locally?

If not, why not?

Where can you do any of these activities in this area?

_____

_____

_____

_____

Improving our area

This topic web shows possible curriculum links but we will not have thought of everything so you may like to add some of your own.

MUSIC
- Play 6 contrasting pieces of music – children to discuss which best suits the view from school, giving reasons for their choice. Do not give information about the music until after the choices have been made.

LITERACY
- Non-fiction writing
- Poetry based on the immediate locality
(Worksheet 3)

NUMERACY
- Measurement and scale in simple map work
(Worksheet 1, 2,)

SCIENCE
- Link to DT work on making a model of a local building and installing a simple light circuit

PE
- Links to map work on 'outdoor and adventurous activities'

HISTORY
- Investigating the locality in the past and changes that have taken place
(Worksheet 4)

ICT
- Create repeating patterns linked with art work

Improving our area

DT
- Making a model of a building that can be seen from school; making a simple circuit with a bulb to light up the inside

ART
- Sketching patterns from the immediate environment – using these as a basis for printing and other forms of symmetrical pattern making

Improving our area

(QCA Unit 21: How can we improve the area we can see from our window?)

This work builds on the work carried out in Year 3 concerning the view from the window. To assist pupils in considering how improvements could be made to the local area they are encouraged to understand maps and to make their own maps.

Worksheets 1 and 2 (ART) encourage the understanding of the differences between pictures and maps and provide revision of work with keys. It is important that pupils should discuss this work before starting. This will give opportunities for adults to point out, if necessary, the lack of need to show separate buildings on small scale maps and that no sky is shown on maps and plans. The view from your school window may show a very large area or a very small area but both are equally valid for this activity. Of course, if possible, you may be able to choose a window that gives a view that is particularly suitable for drawing, then converting to a plan or map.

Worksheet 3 (LITERACY) asks pupils to select a small area in their locality and to draw a map of it, labelling particular features that could be improved. They could show features that exist already and that could be improved – empty buildings, rubbish tips, etc. Or they could show features that they would like to have introduced to the area – playgrounds, gardens, etc.

Worksheet 4 (HISTORY) links with the history topic on life in the locality in the past. It can also be used alongside the topic concerning what life was like for children in World War 2. We recommend that this sheet is used by pupils working in pairs. The sheet is divided into four sections: the first section is where the children should write a summary of what they think the school area was like in the past. It would then be very useful for pupils to find out as much information as possible about the school area before continuing with the second section. You or your classroom assistant may be able to give them some information; there may be members of staff in your school who remember the area from some time ago or you may find a local resident who would be willing to come in to talk to the class – the pupils could listen and make notes while the resident is talking to them, provided she/he is aware that they may do so.

The third section asks the pupils to give their opinions about the area and the fourth section invites them to suggest plans for the future. As a final activity the children can prepare a short 'speech' to present to the class, summarising what they have found out and what proposals they would have for the future. You may like to restrict the time allowed for this activity – perhaps suggesting that each child or pair of children can have just one minute to present their information.

Improving our area 1

Name: Date:

Look at the two pictures below.

Now look at the map below. It gives a 'bird's eye view' of one of the places shown in the two pictures.

 Which of the two photographs does the plan represent? _____

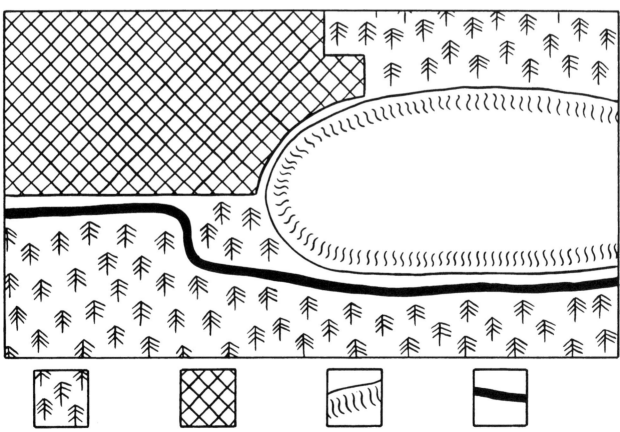

 Use appropriate colours to shade the map. Don't forget to colour the key to match.

Improving our area 2

Name: Date:

✎ In this box, draw a picture of the view from your school window.

✎ In this box, draw a map of the area that you drew.
Add a key to your map.

Map

Key

Andrew Brodie: Across the Curriculum Geography 8–9 © A & C Black Publishers Ltd

Improving our area 3

Name: Date:

In the box below draw a plan or map of an area near your school.

Try to identify things that could be improved in that area and label them on your map.

Improving our area 4

Name: _____   Date: _____

Look at the view from your school.

What do you think has changed in the last fifty years?
Write your ideas below.

_____

_____

_____

_____

Discuss the changes with your teacher or classroom assistant.
What can they tell you about how the area used to be?

_____

_____

_____

_____

Do you think the area is better now than it was or do you think it is
worse? Give reasons for your ideas.

_____

_____

_____

_____

How would you like your area to change in the future, or would
you like it to stay the same? Again, give reasons for your ideas.

_____

_____

_____

_____

Read through all the notes that you have written on this page.
Can you create a short, interesting speech for the rest of your class
to listen to?

What's in the news?

(QCA Unit 16: What's in the news?)

We have not produced a topic web for this topic due to its narrow focus.

Worksheets 1 and 2 (**LITERACY**) are based on a world weather forecast. In addition to the geographical context, this work contributes to the speaking and listening element of English work. It also provides the opportunity to consider climates of different parts of the world and seasonal differences between the hemispheres.

Resources:

This work is particularly effective if children are given the opportunity to watch one of the daily world weather forecasts that can be seen on television. If these are not available encourage the children to watch local or national weather forecasts, focussing on the spoken language and body language of the presenter.

Extension activity:

Ask pupils to look at the weather symbols used in a variety of daily newspapers, then set the task of inventing a weather map for either:

a) The British Isles,
b) Europe,
c) The world.

If possible, some of these fictional weather maps could be photocopied on to OHP transparencies, then pupils could be invited to come to the front of the class and present the weather forecast. Pupils should be encouraged to practise first, familiarising themselves with the names of some countries and continents so that they can talk with confidence about the map.

What's in the news? 1

Name: _____

Date: _____

Look at the world weather map on Worksheet 2. The weather symbols show you what the weather was like in some parts of the world on one particular day.

Discuss with a partner the information shown on the map.

✎ Mark the equator on the map.

✎ Add the names of countries or continents near to the weather symbols. You may use an atlas to help you.

✎ Now prepare a weather report to present to the rest of the class. Your weather report could be for your area, for the British Isles, for Europe or even for the whole world!

It may help to watch some television weather reports. Listen carefully to some of the words and phrases used by television weather reporters.

Here are a few words and phrases that you may like to use in your report, but you may have some better ideas of your own.

> unbroken sunshine   sunny spells   cloudy   showers
>
> persistent rain   clear periods   heavy snow

Andrew Brodie: Across the Curriculum Geography 8–9 © A & C Black Publishers Ltd

What's in the news? 2

Name: Date:

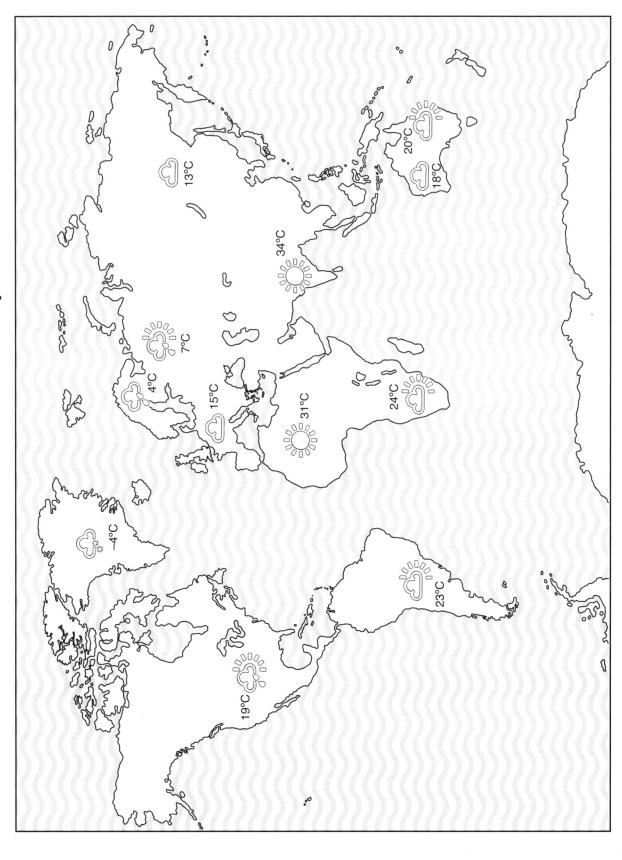

World weather map

Connections across the world

CURRICULUM LINKS

This topic web shows possible curriculum links but we will not have thought of everything so you may like to add some of your own.

LITERACY
- Write a letter to someone in a school in another part of the country describing your locality – encouraging use of geographical vocabulary – send by email or fax
(Worksheet 4)

IT
- Presenting graphs and charts
- Use of email and fax

NUMERACY
- Handling data – tables, charts and graphs
(Worksheet 1, 2, 3)

Connections across the world

HISTORY
- Write a letter from a Roman recently arrived in Britain in mid-winter – consider how this letter may be delivered

SCIENCE
- Keeping warm
- Look at how buildings in different places are built to keep in the warmth or to keep rooms cool

Connections across the world

(QCA Unit 18: Connecting ourselves to the world)

Worksheet 1 (NUMERACY) introduces pupils to some ideas about collecting weather data. It would be very helpful to take the children outside and to discuss estimates of wind force using the information shown on the sheet. They would also benefit from estimating cloud cover using the numbers zero, one quarter, half, three quarters and one.

Worksheets 2 and 3 (NUMERACY) have a weather-based task focusing on extracting information from recorded data. The children will have gained experience by examining the weather conditions on their visit to the school grounds, using the information on worksheet 1 but please note that on worksheet 2 the wind conditions are recorded as wind speeds in miles per hour rather than as wind forces. The answer to both the questions on the page is Day 13; pupils can be encouraged to consider why this is so. The fact that the day was sunny because there was no cloud cover will not be obvious to them. The wind speed was also low on Day 13.

Question 6 on sheet 3 can be used as a starting point for pupils' own data collecting in relation to weather. Ideally if it is possible to establish a contact with another school in a contrasting area or indeed another country, the two classes can swap weather data. The answers to the questions on sheet 3 are as follows:

1. 20
2. complete cloud cover
3. 9
4a. Day 17
4b. 33 miles per hour
5. In the autumn as the weather was generally cloudy, cool and breezy and it was gradually becoming cooler.
6. Daily newspaper records/daily television or radio reports/collection of own readings using appropriate equipment.

Worksheet 4 (LITERACY) is for OHP/group use and introduces the idea of contact via email or fax with a class elsewhere. It emphasises the importance of using geographical vocabulary. You may wish to discuss the difference between facts and opinions.

The weather element of this work provides links to history work on settlers and to the Year 4 science topic on keeping warm.

Connections across the world 1

Name: _____   Date: _____

There are many aspects of the weather that we can **measure**. For example, we measure temperature using a thermometer.

There are some aspects that we can **estimate**. For example we estimate cloud cover by looking at the sky and deciding approximately what fraction is covered by cloud. Another estimate we can make is for wind force.

Wind force	Description	What to look for
0	calm	smoke rises vertically
1	light air	smoke moves in a particular direction but wind vanes stay still
2	light breeze	wind felt on face; leaves rustle on trees
3	gentle breeze	leaves and small twigs moving
4	moderate breeze	small branches move; dust and loose paper blow about
5	fresh breeze	small leafy trees begin to sway
6	strong breeze	large branches move; umbrellas used with difficulty
7	near gale	whole trees in motion; difficult to walk against the wind
8	gale	breaks twigs off trees; walking very difficult
9	strong gale	chimney pots and roof tiles removed
10	storm	trees uprooted; buildings damaged
11	violent storm	much damage caused
12	hurricane	countryside devastated

What do you think the wind force number is today? _____

Connections across the world 2  NUMERACY

Name: Date:

The table below shows a set of weather readings taken over a period of twenty days. It includes the temperature, cloud cover and wind speed. The wind speeds are shown in miles per hour and not as estimated wind forces.

Day	1	2	3	4	5	6	7	8	9	10
Wind speed (m.p.h)	11	8	18	14	11	9	12	6	10	11
Cloud cover*	1	$\frac{1}{2}$	$\frac{1}{2}$	$\frac{3}{4}$	$\frac{1}{2}$	1	$\frac{3}{4}$	1	1	$\frac{1}{4}$
Temperature °C	13	10	11	10	10	12	13	11	10	9

Day	11	12	13	14	15	16	17	18	19	20
Wind speed (m.p.h)	17	10	4	7	28	30	33	19	14	12
Cloud cover*	$\frac{3}{4}$	1	0	$\frac{1}{4}$	$\frac{1}{2}$	$\frac{1}{2}$	$\frac{1}{2}$	$\frac{1}{4}$	$\frac{1}{4}$	$\frac{1}{2}$
Temperature °C	9	7	15	11	7	9	9	5	6	4

* cloud cover

   1 = complete cover

   $\frac{3}{4}$ = mainly cloudy

   $\frac{1}{2}$ = partially cloudy

   $\frac{1}{4}$ = a little cloudy

 Can you work out which day had the highest temperature? _____

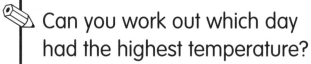 The day with the least cloud cover must have been the sunniest day. Which day was that? _____

Connections across the world 3

Name: _____   Date: _____

You will need the table of weather
readings on Worksheet 2 to answer
some of these questions.

1. For how many days was weather data collected? _____

2. Were there more days of complete cloud cover or of completely
    clear skies?

    _____

    _____

    _____

3. How many days had a temperature of less than 10°C? _____

4(a) On which day was the wind strongest? _____

  (b) What was the wind speed on that day?_____

5. In which season of the year do you think that this data was
    collected? Give reasons for your answer.

    _____

    _____

    _____

    _____

6. Suggest ways that you could collect weather data in your area.

    _____

    _____

    _____

    _____

Connections across the world 4

Name: Date:

You are going to write to someone in another area of this country or in another country. (Your teacher will tell you which.)

Tell the person you are writing to about the area where you live.
Use geographical words in your letter.
The letter should contain facts, not your opinion.

You could use some of the vocabulary below to help you with your letter.

WORD BANK

area   mountainous   valley   city   physical features   village

town   climate   rural   hilly   flat   industrial   urban

locality   countryside   seaside

 Make some notes about what you are going to include in your letter.

_____

_____

_____

_____

When the letter is ready you can send it to the recipient by email or fax.

Our whole world

This topic web shows possible curriculum links but we will not have thought of everything so you may like to add some of your own.

ICT
- Potential use of web-cams for observing other parts of the world

LITERACY
- Vocabulary of names of some of the world's continents, oceans and countries
(Worksheet 1)
- Use of capital letters for place names
- Reading clues about places
(Worksheet 2, 3, 4, 5)

NUMERACY
- Comparisons of distances

ART
- Patterns in textiles and printing from other cultures
- Drawing, painting, printing and collage to produce artwork about a journey

RE
- Opportunities for discussion in relation to religious centres in the world, eg Mecca, Jerusalem

Our whole world

HISTORY
- Invaders and settlers – where did these people come from?
- Ancient Egypt

PE
- Dance, using world music

MUSIC
- Chinese music, exploring pentatonic scales (note that not all music using pentatonic scales is Chinese music)

Our whole world

(QCA Unit 24: Passport to the world)

Worksheet 1 (LITERACY) is a map of the world. Pupils are required to write on the names of some countries. They should also locate the British Isles, recognising the shape. The countries to be shown include:

Egypt, as Ancient Egypt is likely to be covered during Year 3 or Year 4;

Italy, as the Romans will be considered during Year 3 or Year 4;

Norway – you may also like to show the pupils the positions of Sweden and Denmark to enable them to see where the Vikings came from;

China, as you may be studying Chinese music in Year 3 or Year 4;

India, as pupils will be studying a village in India.

The other countries are:

> *United States of America* (which can be shown as USA)
> *Australia*
> *Brazil*

The initial letters of each country are shown. You should write the full names on the whiteboard so that pupils can see them when completing this activity. Pupils can finish the map by lightly shading the land green and the sea blue. A valuable discussion could centre around which countries are closer to the British Isles and which countries are further away.

Worksheets 2 to 5 (LITERACY) are all designed to address the QCA recommendation that pupils could participate in a game to identify a city or location when provided with two clues each day for a week – see QCA Unit 24, 'Passport to the World'. This is very time consuming for teachers so we are providing three sets of clues on sheets 2 to 4, then a pupil entry sheet on sheet 5. Sheet 2 gives clues about Rome; Sheet 3 about New York; Sheet 4 about Cairo.

Each sheet is designed so that you can photocopy it then cut the copy into five pieces, each containing two clues. You may decide to spread the games over the year, perhaps completing the Rome game in the autumn, New York in the spring and Cairo in the summer; or you may like to complete them over a total period of three consecutive weeks.

Please note that sheet 5 could be used with your own clues for other locations – for example some clues about the school's location. Before completing Sheet 2, pupils should be introduced to the term 'peninsula' as an area of land that juts out into a lake or sea so is nearly surrounded by water. To assist pupils with spellings we suggest that you display a word bank of city names, including the three cities featured in these games.

Our whole world 1

Name: Date:

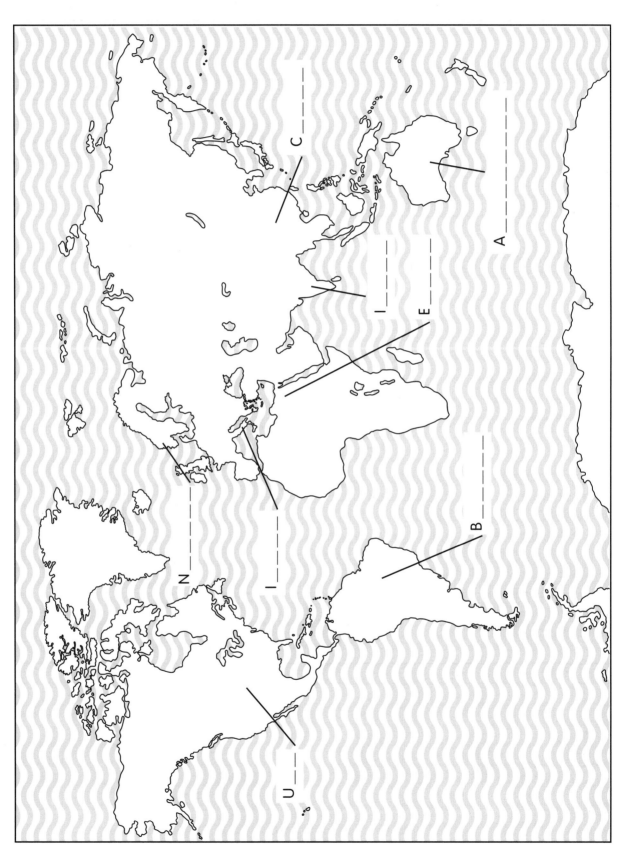

The World

Our whole world 2

Name: Date:

Which city is this?   Game 1

 This is a city in Europe.

 It is in the southern part of Europe.

 This city is in a country that forms a peninsula in the Mediterranean Sea.

 Some people think that the country is shaped like a boot.

 This city was the centre of a huge empire.

 People from this city and the area around it invaded most of Europe approximately two thousand years ago.

 The centre of the Catholic Church is based in this city at a place called the Vatican.

 The Vatican is a very small separate country within this city.

 The city is the capital city of Italy.

 The city was named after a man called Romulus.

Our whole world 3

Name: Date:

Which city is this? Game 2

 This is a very big city.

 It is not in this country.

 You can travel to it by aeroplane or you could sail into its harbour on a large liner.

 It is situated on the coast of the Atlantic Ocean.

 This city used to be called New Amsterdam.

 It is built mainly on islands, joined together by bridges.

 It has lots of tall buildings called skyscrapers.

 One famous building is called the Empire State Building.

 This city is in the United States of America.

 It is not the capital city of the USA.

Our whole world 4

Name: Date:

Which city is this?   Game 3

 This city is in the continent of Africa.

 It is an important port.

 This city is the capital of its country.

 The country is in the North of Africa.

 The city is a port on a river; the longest river in the world.

 Nearby there are sandy deserts.

 This city is a port on the River Nile.

 It is close to Giza where there are huge pyramids.

 Approximately eight million people live in this city.

 This city is in Egypt.

Our whole world 5

Name: _____   Date: _____

Do you know which city this is?
Here are the clues:

CLUE 1 _____
_____

CLUE 2 _____
_____

CLUE 1 _____
_____

CLUE 2 _____
_____

CLUE 1 _____
_____

CLUE 2 _____
_____

CLUE 1 _____
_____

CLUE 2 _____
_____

CLUE 1 _____
_____

CLUE 2 _____
_____

I think that this city is _____

Geography and numbers

(QCA Unit 25: Geography and numbers)

We have not included a topic web with this unit as the sheets are, of course, designed to provide links between geography and numeracy rather than with a wide range of subjects.

Worksheet 1 (**NUMERACY**) features the four points of the compass and invites children to create their own mnemonics for remembering these. Please note that the term 'mnemonic' is introduced officially at Year 6 in the Literacy Strategy. However, it is highly relevant to this Year 4 activity.

Worksheet 2 (**NUMERACY**) extends the pupils' knowledge of the points of the compass to include the four midpoints: North-East, South-East, South-West and North-West. Before working on the sheet the children should be reminded that right angles are 90° and that half right angles are 45°. A worthwhile introductory activity would be to ask the pupils to:

stand facing north, then turn through 90° clockwise;
stand facing north, then turn through 45° clockwise;
stand facing north, then turn through 90° and 45° clockwise;
stand facing north, then turn through 90° and 90° and 45° clockwise;
etc.

Practice of adding multiples of 90 or multiples of 45 would also be very valuable.

Worksheet 3 (**NUMERACY**) shows a wind direction chart, a useful source for data interpretation. Children will observe that the most common wind direction was South-West, which is the prevailing wind direction in the British Isles. They are asked to state the number of days in January – they may know this already but can also work it out by counting the number of shaded squares on the chart. The fractions that they are asked to identify are as follows:

West: $\frac{6}{31}$

North-East: $\frac{1}{31}$

North-West: $\frac{4}{31}$

This is a useful exercise in demonstrating that the 'total' becomes the denominator (ie. 31) and the part that we are asking about becomes the numerator. The fact that 31 is a prime number makes the questions less complicated than they would be if the fractions could be simplified.

Geography and numbers 1

Name: Date:

We can label the four main points of the compass by working clockwise in this order: North, East, South, West

To remember the order we can use a mnemonic. A mnemonic is a clue that helps us remember.

Here is a well-known mnemonic for the points of the compass ⟶

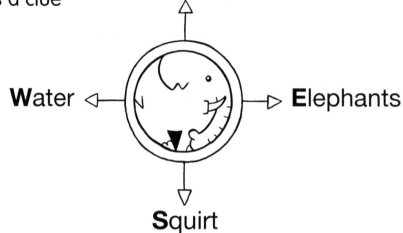

Here is another mnemonic for the points of the compass:

Never Enter Spooky Woods

Try to make up three of your own mnemonics for the points of compass.

1. _____

2. _____

3. _____

Choose your favourite mnemonic to label these compass points.

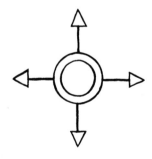

Geography and numbers 2

Name: Date:

We have looked at the four main points of the compass.
Between these points are other points.

For example, between North and East there is North-East.

WORD BANK

North, South, East, West,

North-West, North-East,

South-West, South-East

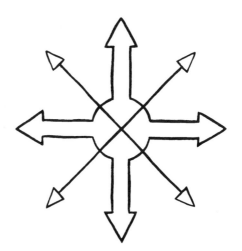

Label the compass with the eight points in the
correct places.
Now answer these questions:

If I face North then turn clockwise to face North-
East, through how many degrees have I turned? —————

If I face North then turn clockwise to face South,
through how many degrees have I turned? —————

If I face North then turn clockwise to face South-
East, through how many degrees have I turned? —————

Geography and numbers 3

Name: Date:

Jasdeep recorded the direction that the wind came from every day in the month of January.

She drew a chart to show her results.

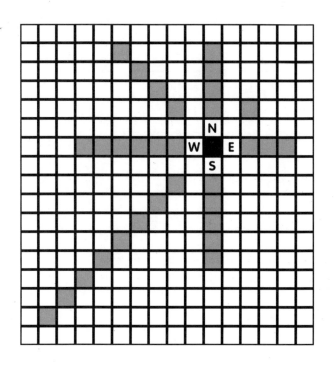

✏ Now answer these questions about Jasdeep's chart.

1. On how many days was the wind from:

   the North? _____   the South? _____

   the East? _____   the West? _____

2. What was the most common direction
   from which the wind came? _____

3. From which direction did the wind not come? _____

4. How many days are there in January? _____

5. For what fraction of the days in January did the wind come from:

   the West? _____   the North-East? _____

   the North-West? _____

    Andrew Brodie: Across the Curriculum Geography 8–9 © A & C Black Publishers Ltd